BASIC RULES
OF
GRAMMAR

BOOK 4

	Beginning	Book 1	Book 2	Book 3	Book 4
Adjectives and descriptions	35, 36, 40	29, 30, 31, 34, 41, 48	29, 30, 31, 34	11, 12, 13, 14, 15, 18	11, 13, 18
Adverbs			41, 48	22, 23, 26	15, 16, 18
Alphabet	44, 45	44, 45, 46, 48	27, 28, 34	38, 40	17, 18
Antonyms (opposites)	37		35, 36, 40, 48	16, 18	
Apostrophes				24, 25, 26, 46, 48	22, 26, 46
Capital letters		6, 7, 8, 10	6, 10	27, 34, 46, 48	7, 46, 48
Classification/Sorting	33, 34		37, 40		23,26
Colloquialisms					29, 34
Commas		35, 40	39	45, 48	20, 21, 26
Conjunctions		14, 18	42, 48	37, 40	25, 26
Exclamation marks				31, 34	32
Full stops		6, 7	5, 6, 10	46, 48	19, 46
Homonyms/Homophones/ Commonly confused words		42, 48	38, 40	35, 36, 40	24, 41, 48
Instructions/Information				44	37, 39, 40
Nouns		13, 15			
common	4, 5, 8, 9, 10	16, 17, 18, 19, 20, 21, 25, 26, 37, 40	11, 12, 18	4, 6, 10	4, 10, 42
proper		23, 24, 25, 26	13, 14, 18	4, 10, 27	4, 10
collective					5, 6, 10
Paragraphs					38
Prefixes/Suffixes			46	41, 42, 48	43, 44, 45, 46, 48
Prepositions	14, 15, 16, 17, 18	36, 40	43	39, 40	
Pronouns			16, 18	7, 10	9, 10
Questions/Answers	19, 20, 21, 22, 23, 26	32, 33, 34	24, 25, 26	28, 31, 32, 34	31, 33
Rhyme	46, 48	43, 48		33, 34	
Sentences/Sequencing	6, 7, 10, 11, 12, 13, 18, 24, 25, 27, 28, 30, 31, 32, 34	4, 5, 6, 7, 9, 10, 11	4, 7, 8, 9, 10	17, 44, 47	12, 35, 36, 37, 39, 40
Similes				9, 10	23, 28, 34
Singular/Plural	29, 34	22, 26	15, 18	5	8, 10
Speech/Dialogue		47, 48	32, 33, 34	29, 30, 32, 34	30, 31, 32, 33, 34
Syllabication			44, 45, 48	43, 48	47, 48
Synonyms			47, 48	8	27
Verbs/Root words in verbs	38, 39, 40, 41, 42, 43, 48	34	17, 19, 20, 21, 22, 23, 26	19, 20	42, 48
Verb tenses			20, 26	21, 26	14, 18
Vowels	47, 48	12, 13			

Contents

Editors: Alison Millar and Alison MacTier   Cover image: Barrie Richardson
Layout artist: Patricia Hollingsworth   Cover design: Kim Ashby and Design for Marketing, Ware

© 1996 Folens Limited, on behalf of the authors.
Every effort has been made to contact copyright holders of material used in this book. If any have been overlooked, we will be pleased to make any necessary arrangements.

British Library in Publication Data. A catalogue record for this book is available from the British Library.

First published 1996 by Folens Limited, Dunstable and Dublin.
Folens Limited, Albert House, Apex Business Centre, Boscombe Road, Dunstable, LU5 4RL, England.

ISBN 1 85276235 7

Printed in Great Britain

Nouns

Nouns are **names**.

Common nouns are **names** of things: girl, city, month, car, house.
Proper nouns are **names** of **people**, **animals**, **places**, **dates**,
brand names and **titles**: John, Goldie, The Mill House, London,
April, Saab, The Bible.

A Write the **common nouns** that are the answers to the following:

1. A person who makes things from wood.
2. A place where books are kept.
3. An animal whose young are called tadpoles.
4. An instrument for looking at small objects.
5. A person who designs buildings.
6. A place where people watch films.
7. An animal in legends. It has one horn.
8. Something that is used for cutting cloth.

B Copy these sentences and underline the **proper nouns**:

1. Rover the dog swam across the wide river.
2. Fluffy was playing happily with a ball of wool.
3. Sam enjoyed going to Brighton.
4. A truck towed the broken-down Ford car along the road.
5. Sean Connery appeared in many films as British spy James Bond.
6. We went to York to visit Aunt Jane.
7. Jan and Mia saw Mr Singh catch the thief.
8. The lion escaped from its cage in Whipsnade Zoo.
9. Mrs Pierce shouted loudly at the barking dog.
10. Old Jock walked slowly along West Street.

C Write three **nouns** for each of the following groups. The first one is done for you.

Group	Nouns		
fish	trout	shark	mackerel
dogs			
countries			
vegetables			
cities			
toys			
insects			
fruit			
flowers			
sports			
farm animals			

Collective nouns

Sometimes we need a particular **noun** for a group of things.
These are called **collective nouns**.

Example: a **troop** of soldiers.

A   Finish off each phrase by using one of the words in the box.
The first one is done for you.

1. a flock of sheep	2. a pack of
3. a fleet of	4. a swarm of
5. a crowd of	6. a squadron of
7. a herd of	8. a library of
9. a babble of	10. a wardrobe of
11. a bunch of	12. a clump of
13. a string of	14. a ream of
15. a team of	16. a choir of
17. a school of	18. a crew of
19. a pride of	20. a shoal of

cattle
voices
footballers
sheep
books
ships
fish
sailors
whales
cards
flowers
clothes
paper
aeroplanes
grass
bees
singers
people
beads
lions

B   On your own, or with a friend, think up some new **collective nouns** for these:

1. a ____ of clocks
2. a ____ of sweets
3. a ____ of teachers
4. a ____ of robots
5. a ____ of hamsters
6. a ____ of garden gnomes
7. a ____ of racing cars
8. a ____ of fleas
9. a ____ of skyscrapers
10. a ____ of dinosaurs

Groups and collective nouns

A   Write one name for each of the following sets:

1.   fir, oak, ash, chestnut – **trees**
2.   shark, salmon, trout, plaice
3.   Alps, Rockies, Himalayas, Pennines
4.   Atlantic, Pacific, Indian, Arctic
5.   Japan, Ireland, Greenland, France
6.   New York, Moscow, Peking, Dublin
7.   canoe, punt, barge, catamaran
8.   guitar, flute, violin, mandolin
9.   viper, python, cobra, asp
10.   Pluto, Venus, Mars, Saturn

B   Make an interesting sentence with each of the following:

1.   The **fleet** of ships ...
2.   A **clump** of trees ...
3.   The **shoal** of herring ...
4.   The **flock** of sheep ...
5.   A **herd** of buffaloes ...
6.   The **kennel** of dogs ...
7.   The **litter** of pups ...
8.   An **army** of soldiers ...
9.   The **class** of children ...
10.   A **choir** of angels ...

C   What would you find in these groups? A thesaurus or dictionary will help.

1.   bunch
2.   parliament
3.   hand
4.   nest
5.   gaggle
6.   pod
7.   swarm
8.   rising
9.   litter
10.   congregation
11.   skein
12.   forest

Basic Rules of Grammar: Book 4

Capital letters

Capital letters are used for:
(i) the **start** of a **sentence**
(ii) **I** when used on its own
(iii) **proper nouns**.

My teacher is very intelligent.
I was sick, so I went to bed.
Dan bought a Rolls Royce in May.
Mr and Mrs Patel went to Wales.
Sir Henry Peters spoke to Dr Jones.
Divali begins on Thursday.

A Re-write the following sentences.
Insert the **capital letters** where needed.

1. at the end of every sentence there is a full stop.

2. she is older than i.

3. yesterday shazia sian was absent from school.

4. i have a baby brother named alan.

5. peaches and bananas are delicious fruits.

6. saqib and i went to the cinema on tuesday.

7. dr daly and lord carter live in manchester.

8. alankar and raymond are in the library.

9. we write in our diaries every day.

10. i hope you like our new office.

11. i have a friend called manjinder.

12. i invited anne to my party.

13. last thursday the school team won the chess final.

14. we do not go to school on christmas day.

15. muslims all over the world celebrate ramadan.

16. november comes between october and december.

17. muriel's mother made pancakes on shrove tuesday.

18. my summer holidays lasted from june to september.

19. we went to the seaside for the easter bank holiday.

20. in america the fourth of july is called independence day.

21. april the first is called april fools' day.

22. peter's best friend was born on new year's day.

23. there are two songs that i like.

24. i wrote to aunt jeanette on saturday.

Plurals

Singular means one. Plural means more than one.
Read the rules about making plurals.
Write the plurals of the words.

Rules	Singular
A Most nouns become **plural** by adding **s** to the **singular**.	1. dog 2. eye 3. step
B Nouns ending in **ch**, **s**, **sh**, **ss** and **x** become **plural** by adding **es**.	1. circus 2. church 3. bench
C Nouns ending in **y** with a consonant before, change the **y** to **ies** in the **plural**.	1. lady 2. baby 3. family
D Nouns ending in **y** with a vowel before, become **plural** by adding **s**.	1. donkey 2. valley 3. monkey
E A few nouns ending in **f** or **fe** change to **ves** in the **plural**.	1. half 2. knife 3. self
F A number of nouns become **plural** by changing the vowel sound and spelling.	1. foot 2. mouse 3. woman
G Nouns ending in **o** with a vowel before become **plural** by adding **s**.	1. radio 2. patio 3. cuckoo
H Nouns ending in **o** with a consonant before, often become **plural** by adding **es**.	1. potato 2. volcano 3. hero
I Some nouns are the same in the **singular** and **plural**.	1. deer 2. fish 3. sheep

Pronouns

A **pronoun** is used in place of a **noun**.

Example: **Trevor** has a new **computer**. **He** likes to play games on **it**.

Here is a list of personal **pronouns**:

1st person	singular	I	me	my, mine
2nd person	singular	you	you	your, yours
3rd person	singular	he, she, it	him, her, it	his, hers, its
1st person	plural	we	us	our, ours
2nd person	plural	you	you	your, yours
3rd person	plural	they	them	their, theirs

A Copy this passage changing some of the **nouns** to **pronouns** to cut down the repetition:

Trevor received a new computer for Christmas. Trevor had also got two games for Trevor's computer. Trevor couldn't wait to try the games. First of all Trevor put the 'Space Attack' disc in, but the disc would not load. Trevor tried the other disc but the other disc would not load either. Trevor was furious. Just then, Trevor's father came into the room. Trevor told Trevor's father that the games wouldn't load and Trevor's dad looked carefully at the games. Suddenly Trevor's father laughed. "The games are for a different make of computer. Never mind, I'll change these games tomorrow!"

B Read this extract from a school booklet:

When your child comes to St Thomas' School he will learn the basic skills of reading, writing and numeracy. He will need a pair of plimsolls for PE and a schoolbag for books and pencils. It will be helpful if all clothes have name labels. We hope your child will be happy at St Thomas' School.

But there are boys and girls at St Thomas'!
Re-write it so that the girls do not feel left out!

Test 1

A Write one **noun** for each of the following sets.

Example: viper, python, cobra ... snakes.

1. England, France, Italy, Spain, Portugal
2. Thames, Severn, Shannon, Nile, Mississippi
3. guitar, violin, cello, banjo, viola
4. spanner, saw, hammer, screwdriver, drill

B Copy and complete these with **collective nouns**:

1. a ☐ of wolves
2. a ☐ of whales
3. a ☐ of sheep
4. a ☐ of people
5. a ☐ of flowers
6. a ☐ of books

C Write the **plural** of each of these words:

1. hand	2. pen	3. elf
4. brush	5. pear	6. hoof
7. lorry	8. potato	9. daisy
10. key	11. cherry	12. child
13. shelf	14. leaf	15. adult
16. mouse	17. goose	18. fungus
19. tomato	20. glass	21. cactus
22. sheep	23. mummy	24. octopus

D Copy this passage replacing some of the **nouns** with **pronouns**:

Angelo ate an orange. Angelo gave Peter an apple.
Then Angelo and Peter saw Mr Harris in the garden.
Mr Harris said, "Hello!" to Angelo and Peter.

Description builders

Descriptions can be built up following a set pattern.

Example:

Begin with a noun: The rock

Add an adjective: The large rock

Add another: The large, grey rock

And another: The large, grey, jagged rock

Add a verb: The large, grey, jagged rock rolled

Add an adverb: The large, grey, jagged rock rolled lumberingly

Add an ending: The large, grey, jagged rock rolled lumberingly down the mountain

Add an adjective
to the ending: The large, grey, jagged rock rolled lumberingly down the steep mountain

Add another: The large, grey, jagged rock rolled lumberingly down the steep, slippery mountain.

A   Try writing a description in this way:

Begin with a noun

   Add an adjective

      Add another

        And another

           Add a verb

              Add an adverb

                Add an ending

                  Add an adjective to the ending

                    Add another

Sentence portraits

A Close your eyes and imagine a person that you know.
Write a short **sentence** about that person.

Example: He is my best friend.
   or   I have always liked the way you smile.

Add more **sentences**. Choose some ideas from the list below.

1.   Write a sentence with a colour in it.
2.   Write a sentence with a part of the body in it.
3.   Write a very short sentence.
4.   Write a sentence with 'because' in it.
5.   Write a sentence that ends with an exclamation mark.
6.   Write a sentence with a piece of clothing in it.
7.   Write a sentence with an adjective and an adverb in it.
8.   Write a very long sentence.
9.   Write a sentence with 'but' in it.
10. Write a sentence with an animal in it.
11. Write a sentence with 'looks like' in it.
12. Write a sentence in which two or more words begin with the same sound.
13. Write a sentence with a question mark at the end.
14. Write a sentence with two commas in it.
15. Write a sentence with a wish in it.
16. Write a sentence with a feeling in it.

B When you have finished you will have something like this:

> Susan was my friend.
> Her hair was blonde.
> She had long fingers.
> She was tall.
> I really admired her because
> she could juggle.
> How she could dance!

C Redraft your work to improve it.

Make up a title.

Add more words or sentences.

Take out or change anything that you do not like.

Put the sentences in a different order.

Check and re-write your work.

Comparative and superlative adjectives

When we compare **two things**, we add **er** to the **adjective**.

Example: small – small**er**.

We write **more** in front of long **adjectives**.

Example: **more** beautiful.

These are called **comparative adjectives**.

A Make these **adjectives** into **comparative adjectives**:

1. old
2. warm
3. ancient
4. fluffy
5. delicious
6. light
7. heavy
8. comfortable

When we compare **three or more things**, we add **est** to the **adjective**.

Example: fast – fast**est**.

Sometimes the last letter of the **adjective** is doubled.

Example bi**g** – big**gest**.

Y following a **consonant** changes to **i**.

Example sill**y** – sill**iest**.

We put **most** in front of long **adjectives**.

Example: dangerous – **most** dangerous.

These are called **superlative adjectives**.

B Make these **adjectives** into **superlative adjectives**:

1. revolting
2. tuneful
3. easy
4. sad
5. early
6. stupid
7. happy
8. straight
9. colourful
10. speedy

Sometimes the **adjective** changes completely.

Example:

bad   worse   worst   good   better   best

Past tense

The **past tense** of a verb shows something has already happened.

Example: **Present tense** – I walk   **Past tense** – I walked

A   Copy and complete each sentence with one of the **verbs** in the **past tense**.

1. The bird **strolled/prowled/flitted** across the sky.
2. The woodlouse **charged/waded/crawled** under the stone.
3. The small butterfly **hopped/hobbled/hovered** near the rose bushes.
4. The house spider **strode/strolled/scurried** into its web.
5. The fat worm **walked/waddled/wriggled** into its burrow.
6. The golden eagle **grabbed/tore/trapped** the lamb in its talons.

The **past tense** can be written in different ways.

Example: She **did** the test. She **has done** the test.

B   Copy and complete these sentences using a different form of the **past tense**:

1. She **wrote** a letter to her friend. She _____ to her friend.
2. He **went** for a drive. He _____ to visit his aunt.
3. He **came** late last night. He _____ at last.
4. He **gave** her a lovely present. He _____ her a new car.
5. The hungry dog **ate** the meat. The dog _____ its first meal in two days.
6. He **flew** _____ _____ once before.

Passed is a verb _____
Past is a preposition meaning 'by, along, beyond or after.'
The tawny owl flew **past** the window.

C   Write **past** or **passed** _____:

1. Pete _____ _____ _____ _____ the graveyard.
2. The crowd cheered as the queen drove _____ .
3. The proud eagle swooped _____ her nest.
4. Many days _____ before my racing pigeon returned home.
5. They were bitten by mosquitos as they _____ through the woods.
6. At half _____ eight the bus _____ by my house.
7. The bird flew _____ in wide circles and _____ over the marshy swamp.

Adverbs

Adverbs describe **verbs**. In the sentence 'The wolf ran quickly', **ran** is the **verb**, and **quickly** is the **adverb** which tells us **how** the wolf **ran**.

Many **adverbs** are formed from **adjectives** by adding **ly**.

Examples:

Adjective	Adverb
graceful	graceful**ly**
awkward	awkward**ly**
sad	sad**ly**

How did you do in the test?

Badly!

Here are some other **adverbs**:

before	already	there	almost	much
soon	since	everywhere	rather	only
now	here	nowhere	very	quite

A Copy this passage underlining the **adverbs**:

He ran quickly down the street. He looked anxiously left and right. Fortunately everything was quiet. He felt tired and rather unhappy to be running away so soon. He reached the crossroads and stopped. He started again and turned into the High Street. Suddenly he stopped. There was the sound of footsteps behind him. His heart beat violently. He was being followed!

B Copy and complete this passage filling the gaps with **ly adverbs**:

The fishing boat floated ⬚⬚⬚ on the calm ocean. Then Hal saw a

black fin moving ⬚⬚⬚ . It was a shark. He took the oar and beat the

shark ⬚⬚⬚ on the head. The shark thrashed the water ⬚⬚⬚ .

Hal hit it again and the shark sank ⬚⬚⬚ from sight. Hal sat down.

Adverbs

To make an **adjective** into an **adverb** – add **ly**. However, if the word ends in **le** – take away the **le** then add **ly**.

Example: valuab**le** – valuab**ly**.

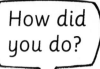

Reasonably!

Horribly!

Terribly!

A Change these **adjectives** into **adverbs**:

1. kind
2. suspicious
3. notable
4. gentle
5. quiet
6. mad
7. light
8. last
9. silent
10. bright

B Change these **adjectives** into **adverbs** that end with **ibly** or **ably**:

1. possible
2. manageable
3. valuable
4. suitable
5. reliable
6. noticeable
7. terrible
8. miserable
9. horrible
10. legible
11. comfortable
12. impossible
13. reasonable
14. visible
15. responsible
16. incredible

C Write sentences that include four of the **adverbs** from **B**.

Alphabetical order

Words can always be arranged in **alphabetical order**.
If the first letters are the same, the **second letters** are used.
If the second letters are the same, the **third letters** are used and so on.

A Read the clues. Finish the words.

1. To divide things up — sep ☐

2. A soldier on guard — sen ☐

3. Someone who serves you — ser ☐

4. Winter is one — sea ☐

5. More than two or three — sev ☐

6. After the first — sec ☐

7. You do this with a needle — sew ☐

8. To grab hold — sei ☐

9. A seat — set ☐

10. Not thinking of others — sel ☐

B Write the words from question **A** in **alphabetical order** according
to the third letter.

C The class register lists the class in **alphabetical order** of surnames.
Write the register for this class:

J. Jones
R. Burns
B. Pasternak
C. Parker
A. Patel
S. Turner
R. Trimmer
J. Brown
B. Butcher
C. Burton
C. Paris
B. Sumner
K. Johnson
P. Anson
R. Summers
P. Anderson
B. Candy
R. Celini
J. Canova

Test 2

A Re-write these sentences. Add some **adjectives** to make them more interesting.

1. The girl got out of bed.
2. The cat chased the birds.
3. The man walked round the garden.
4. The teacher came into the room.

B Copy and complete this chart:

Adjective	Comparative	Superlative
big	bigger	
happy		happiest
	sadder	
beautiful		
	more revolting	

C Change the **verbs** in these sentences into the **past tense**:

1. I give lots of presents.
2. The dog eats the food.
3. The thief runs away.
4. I forget which way to go.
5. I go for a walk.

D Make **adverbs** from these **adjectives**:

1. possible   2. comfortable   3. tidy   4. happy   5. terrible

E Write these words in **alphabetical order**:

service   seldom   seat   several   settle   send

The full stop

Always end a **sentence** with a **full stop**.

A Copy each short passage putting in **capital letters** and **full stops** to make three sentences:

1. the snow lay deep on the ground it was very cold in the tents although the campers had sleeping bags they were not warm

2. we agreed to meet at the shops when I arrived Paul was not there I waited for twenty minutes

3. the robin gave the stick to the squirrel he threw it to the frog the frog took the stick in his mouth and dived into the pond

4. a thick fog covered Dublin last night parts of the city were very badly affected motorists were advised to drive carefully

5. a bad storm blew up at sea all the fishing ships made for the harbour the lighthouse-keeper was worried for their safety

6. he caught the ball he passed it to Jenny she kicked it to Shane who slammed it into the back of the net

7. she lived in a small cottage on the hillside a small stream ran by the house it would dry up in summertime

8. look for a safe place stop and wait look all around and listen before you cross the road

B Correct these paragraphs putting in the **capital letters** and **full stops**:

1. one morning Peter and his hound went hunting red deer they saw a beautiful lady she wore a robe of silk her horse wore shoes of pure gold he had never before seen such a beautiful lady

2. William jumped on the white horse behind the princess as the horse galloped away he waved goodbye to Peter and his hound soon they reached the edge of the sea it opened before them and they passed through he saw strange fish that no man had ever seen before

Basic Rules of Grammar: Book 4

Commas

Commas are used to separate items in a list.

Example: On my desk there is a diary, a pen, a pair of scissors and a ruler.

Note: there is not usually a comma before and.

A   Look at these pictures. Copy and complete the lists using commas.

1. On the table there is ...

2. Through the window I can see ...

B   Complete these lists in the same way, but this time experiment to find the order of words that sounds the best:

1. On the table there is ...

2. Through the window I can see ...

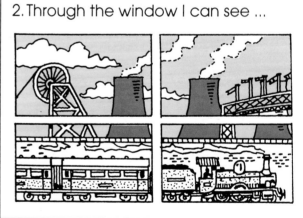

C   Write lists of:

1.   the things in your desk

2.   the people in your family

3.   the things in your pocket

4.   the contents of your wardrobe

5.   the furniture in your bedroom

6.   your friends

Commas

Commas are used before and after **extra information** included in a sentence.

Example: Mr Jones, **our next door neighbour**, kindly threw my ball back.

The sentence would make sense if the **extra information** was removed.

If the **extra information** comes at the end of a sentence, its final **comma** is replaced by the **full stop**.

Example: Our next stop was York, **one of the oldest cities in Britain.**

A   Copy the following **sentences** adding **extra information** from the box:

> a land of mountains and fjords
> the longest river in America
> the friendly old sheep dog
> the head teacher
> my youngest sister
> a large city in England

1. Rover, [   ] , barked at the strangers.

2. The Mississippi, [   ] , flows into the Gulf of Mexico.

3. We visited Norway, [   ] .

4. Susan, [   ] , is five today.

5. Mr Matthews, [   ] , was not amused.

6. Liverpool, [   ] , has two cathedrals.

B   Add **extra information** to these sentences:

1. The actor starred in a smash-hit film.

2. Jenny went to Edinburgh.

Apostrophes: possession

The **apostrophe** is a sign used to show **possession** (belonging to).
Make sure the **apostrophe** goes in the right place.

Add **'** before the **s** for **one**.

Example: Brian**'s** friend (the friend of Brian).

Add **'** after the **s** for **more than one**.

Example: the worker**s'** club (the club of the workers).

If a word ends in **s** already, just add the **apostrophe**.

Example: John Keat**s'** poems (the poems of John Keats).

A   Write two sentences about each of these pictures:

The dog's biscuit

B   Copy the following sentences.
Add **apostrophes** in the correct places.

1.   The gobstopper stuck in the budgies beak.

2.   Brians plan went wrong.

3.   The tea spilled over Grannys pension book.

4.   Draculas teeth glinted in the moonlight.

5.   Gretas breath came in short, nervous gasps.

The natural world

A Complete each sentence with the name of an **animal**:

Example: **Bird** is to nest as **spider** is to web.

1. Pig is to [ ] as sheep is to lamb.
2. Dog is to [ ] as hare is to form.
3. Caterpillar is to butterfly as [ ] is to frog.
4. Kitten is to cat as puppy is to [ ] .
5. Horse is to stable as cow is to [ ] .
6. Paw is to dog as hoof is to [ ] .
7. Shoal is to herring as school is to [ ] .
8. Spider is to fly as cat is to [ ] .

B Choose the correct word.

Example: as busy as an **eel/ape/ant**
          as busy as an **ant**

1. as blind as a **rat/bat/cat**
2. as graceful as a **donkey/swan/elephant**
3. as slow as a **hare/fox/snail**
4. as gentle as a **lamb/hawk/tiger**
5. as strong as a **mule/horse/pig**
6. as swift as a **robin/hawk/crow**
7. as hungry as a **mouse/fox/wolf**
8. as brave as a **monkey/deer/lion**
9. as wise as an **eagle/owl/ostrich**

C Which is the odd one out in the following lists:
Give a reason for each answer.

Example: wren, owl, **bee**, tern, crow. A bee is an insect and not a bird.

1. seal, sheep skunk, sparrow, squirrel
2. pike, trout, whale, herring, cod
3. rabbit, badger, otter, fox, hare
4. peach, pineapple, pear, potato, plum
5. oyster, mussel, octopus, periwinkle, whelk
6. fir tree, yew tree, pine tree, beech tree
7. donkey, kangaroo, mule, ferret
8. magpie, penguin, cuckoo, robin, blackbird
9. stallion, filly, colt, buffalo, foal

Homophones

Homophones are words which **sound the same**, but which are **spelled differently** and have **different meanings**.

Example: The **knight** wore his armour day and **night**.

A Choose the correct **homophone** to complete these sentences:

1. There is a hole in the **sole/soul** of my shoes.
2. Have a **piece/peace** of cake.
3. We had **serial/cereal** for breakfast.
4. A basement can be called a **seller/cellar**.
5. We use a **plum/plumb** line to check that a line is vertical.
6. I live in a house with three **stories/storeys**.
7. Electrical **currents/currants** can be dangerous.
8. **Time/thyme** is a herb.
9. I will need some **course/coarse** sandpaper.

B Write a **homophone** for each of these words.
Give the meanings of each **homophone**.

Example: **road** – a highway, **rode** – the past tense of ride.

1. bored	2. scent
3. steel	4. stare
5. warn	6. meddle
7. write	8. whole
9. allowed	10. waist
11. mined	12. steak
13. peace	14. source
15. sealing	16. idol

C Write each **homophone** in a sentence:

1. which
   witch
2. threw
   through
3. grown
   groan

4. air
   heir
5. pair
   pear
6. bare
   bear

Conjunctions

Conjunctions are used to **connect parts of sentences**.

Example: This tree is an oak **and so** is this one.

Here are some common **conjunctions**:

but	neither	however	therefore
because	although	either	so

A Copy and complete this passage with **conjunctions** from the box.
Try not to use **and** more than once.

The Tunnel

A new tunnel was planned ⬚ there was too much traffic for the only tunnel under the river. ⬚ it would be useful, it would be expensive ⬚ a toll would have to be paid by drivers. ⬚ local people protested about the toll ⬚ they were given special passes. Work was delayed for two months ⬚ there was a flood. ⬚ the flood went down ⬚ the workers soon made up for lost time.

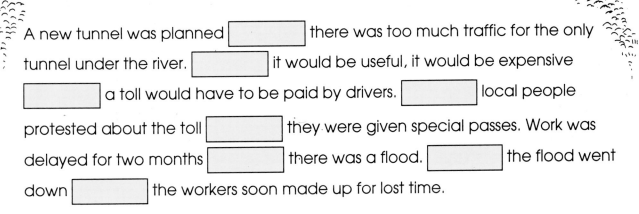

B Here are some less common **conjunctions**:

    nevertheless   notwithstanding   despite

Check their meanings in a dictionary.
Write each one in a sentence.

C List the four **conjunctions** in this paragraph:

Although it was sunny I took an umbrella because there were a few clouds in the distance. It did not rain, however, so I did not need the umbrella.

Test 3

A Choose the correct word from these pairs of **homophones**:

1. Fed up   board/bored

2. A metal   steel/steal

3. The opposite of old   new/knew

4. To speak out loud   allowed/aloud

5. A part of   piece/peace

B Re-write the following using **apostrophes**:

Example: The pencil belonging to Sam – Sam's pencil.

1. The book belonging to John.
2. The books belonging to the children.
3. The biscuit belonging to the dog.
4. The biscuits belonging to the dogs.

C Choose **extra information** for each sentence.
Write the sentences in your book.
Remember to use **commas** correctly.

a shy girl   a big detached house   a rather old man

1. Mr Millar [   ] walked slowly up the stairs.

2. Sarah [   ] said nothing.

3. The building [   ] was destroyed by fire.

D Copy and complete these sentences with **conjunctions**:

1. The dog barked [   ] the cat jumped over the fence.

2. The boy blushed [   ] his trousers were badly torn.

3. It was raining [   ] I still played football.

Synonyms

Words with **similar meanings** are called **synonyms**.

A Sort these words into two lists: happy and sad.

complain	grumble	laugh
smile	grin	giggle
groan	sigh	whine
scowl	moan	smirk
chuckle	chortle	cheer
snigger	whinge	grizzle
grieve	cackle	grimmace

B Write sentences using each of these words:

cried   sobbed   cackled   laughed

C Copy these sentences.
Replace each word in red with a **synonym**.

1. I was **astonished** to see no pictures in the gallery.

2. Write in the **blank** space.

3. The number is at the **foot** of the page.

4. He **glanced** at the skateboard.

5. The two countries were **united** to make one.

6. Swimming is **prohibited** in the lake.

Some words can be used in different ways.

We can **roar** with laughter or with anger.

We can **cry** when we are sad and **cry** out with pleasure.

We can **scream** with pain or with laughter.

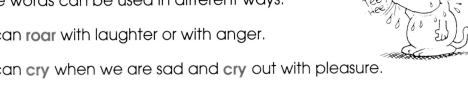

D Write three sentences using other **verbs** that can be used in different ways.

Similes

A **simile** compares two things that are **similar**.

Example: The ballerina was **as light as a feather**.

A Finish these **similes** with words from the box:

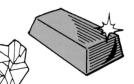

knife	lead	lightning	gold
pancake	rock	crystal	feather

1. as clear as [ ] .
2. as heavy as [ ] .
3. as steady as a [ ] .
4. as light as a [ ] .
5. as sharp as a [ ] .
6. as good as [ ] .
7. as quick as [ ] .
8. as flat as a [ ] .

B These **similes** are mixed up. Sort them out.

1. The sweets were **as sour as honey**.
2. The lime was **as sweet as vinegar**.
3. He is **as round as a rake**.
4. The leaves were **as green as snow**.
5. His face was **as white as grass**.
6. He was **as hot as a cucumber**.
7. She was **as cool as fire**.
8. She is **as thin as a barrel**.

C A **simile** says something is **like** something else. It is a comparison.

Example: as cold **as** ice or she ran **like** the wind.

Invent some **similes**.

1. The snow was as white as [ ] .
2. I felt as happy as [ ] .
3. My home is as cosy as [ ] .
4. I ran like [ ] .
5. The cat was as dead as [ ] .
6. Space is as big as [ ] .
7. He was as old as [ ] .
8. The film was as dull as [ ] .

Colloquialisms

Colloquialisms are **commonly used expressions**.

A The sentences below contain **colloquialisms**. They are in bold type.
Re-write these with words which you think have the same meaning:

1. The audience **cheered their heads off** at the end of the performance.

2. It was **raining cats and dogs**.

3. Jane made **a lightning dash** to school.

4. James was **the apple of his mother's eye**.

5. When the teacher talked about the visit the class **were all ears**.

6. Mike and Sue were always **at loggerheads**.

7. Carol's **heart was in her mouth** when she heard the strange voice.

8. The detective **smelled a rat** when the thief told him where he had got the silver cup from.

9. Mr Smith **kept his wife in the dark** about his plans.

10. After getting all his spellings wrong, Alan had **to face the music**.

B Draw some cartoons to illustrate the **colloquialisms** in **A**.
Ask a friend to guess which ones they are.

Jokes

A These are all jokes about doctors and patients.
The punchlines are mixed up.
Match the punchlines with the jokes.

Patient: Doctor, I've swallowed my pen.	**Doctor:** I'm nervous too. It's the first operation I've done.
Patient: Doctor, when I woke up this morning I swallowed my clock.	**Patient:** That's great! I've never been able to play it before!
Patient: Doctor, I'm nervous because this is my first operation.	**Doctor:** That's OK. Use a pencil.
Doctor: Have you had this before? **Patient:** Yes, doctor.	**Doctor:** Next please!
Patient: Doctor, will I be able to play the guitar after my operation? **Doctor:** Of course.	**Doctor:** There's no need to be alarmed.
Patient: Doctor, no one listens to me.	**Patient:** When did what happen?
Patient: Doctor, I've lost my memory. **Doctor:** When did that happen?	**Doctor:** Who said that?
Patient: Doctor, I think I've become invisible.	**Doctor:** Well, you've got it again.

B Make up some jokes of your own.

Dialogue

A Read this passage aloud. Decide which words are **spoken** by someone.

Only the words that are actually **spoken** by a person need **speech marks** around them.

Where have you been? shouted my Dad. What time of night do you call this? I was very upset. When my Dad shouts at me I feel like crying. I feel such a baby. I've been out with my friends, I said. I took care not to sound too cheeky because that makes Dad go mad. And don't they have homes to go to, he asked, or are you all out on the streets to see what trouble you can find? That's not fair, I cried. We haven't done anything wrong. We only went to the youth club and played snooker. My Dad went red with anger. Look here young man, don't answer me back or I'll take that grin off your face. We have rules in this house, he went on, and when I say you will be back here at ten that is what I mean.

B Re-write the passage using **speech marks**.

Dialogue

Here are two common **dialogue** patterns:

"You shelter in that old house," said Sarah.
"Good idea," answered Paul.

The ghost whispered, "Someone's coming."
Sandra whispered back, "Who is it?"

You could use an **exclamation mark** or a **question mark** instead of
a **full stop** or a **comma**.

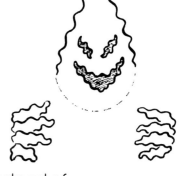

A   Re-write these sentences. Punctuate them using **speech marks**.
Remember the **fulls stops**, **exclamation marks**, **question marks**
and **commas**.

1.   you look like a ghost said sarah

2.   the ghost replied thats because i am a ghost

3.   sarah screamed at the top of her voice a ghost

4.   youre deafening me exclaimed the ghost

5.   sorry said sarah

6.   are you really a ghost asked sarah after a moment

7.   the ghost sighed what do you think

8.   sarah said I can see through you

9.   what do you mean asked the ghost

10. i can see through the trick youre playing laughed sarah

B   Turn the sentences into a story:

Add description and explain
more about how and why the
trick was played on Sarah.

Dialogue

Look at this extract from a children's story.

After a line of description, there are several lines of **dialogue**.

There is a new **paragraph** for each change of **speaker**.

A new **paragraph** begins on a new line and is **indented**.

> Stephen and Tony huddled in the dark cave wishing that the rain would stop.
> "What time is it?" asked Stephen.
> "I don't know," replied Tony, "it's pitch dark and I can't see my watch."
> "Use the torch. It's over there somewhere."
> Tony groped around in the darkness. "It's no good. I can't find it and I've looked everywhere. Are you sure you haven't got it?"
> "Certain."
> "Wait a minute. What's this?"
> "That's not it – it's my foot, you fool!"

A   Take turns with a partner to read aloud the passage below.
The lines of **dialogue** are not written on separate lines.
Can you read it aloud without making any mistakes?

Mr Jones looked at the car longingly. He liked its shape and its bright red paintwork, but he did not like the price tag on the windscreen. The salesman moved in for the kill. This is the car for you sir said the salesman smoothly. Only one owner, perfect condition and very easy on petrol. I don't know, said Mr Jones doubtfully. It's not quite what I had in mind. I wouldn't touch this foreign rubbish if I were you sir answered the salesman quickly. They look good, but they're always letting you down, most unreliable. Still, muttered Mr Jones, this is a bit expensive isn't it? One year's guarantee, sir. Buy one of the others, you'll pay extra in repairs and service. This little beauty will run for years, no danger.

B   Punctuate the passage in **A** and set it out in paragraphs.

C   Write a short **dialogue** using all you have learned about **punctuation** and **paragraphs**.

Test 4

A Write ten diffferent ways of saying **to speak**, for example **mutter** and **shout**.

B Copy and complete each of these **similes**:

1. The snow was like [   ] .

2. The water was as cold as [   ] .

3. The fog was like [   ] .

4. The sun was as hot as [   ] .

C Re-write these sentences.
Replace the **colloquialisms** with words that mean the same.

1. We **fell about laughing**.

2. You need to **keep your wits about you** when climbing mountains.

3. **Keep your eyes peeled** for wasps.

4. I won **by a hair's breadth**.

5. He escaped **by the skin of his teeth**.

6. He was going to dive from the top board but he **chickened out**.

7. Joe **blew his top** when the children ruined his flower beds.

8. We tried to persuade Mrs Jones to let us borrow her scissors, but she would not **give an inch**.

D Write suitable answers. Remember to use **speech marks**.

1. "What are you doing?" the man asked the girl suspiciously.

2. "Why haven't you done your homework?" Mrs Smith asked Sam.

3. "May I help you?" the shop assistant asked the woman as she looked at the dresses on the rack.

4. "What is this supposed to be?" the puzzled onlooker asked the artist as she looked at his picture.

5. "Where shall I dump them?" the lorry driver asked the manager on the building site.

Put them in order

A There are five words in each row.
Write them in **order**, smallest first.

1. minute, week, second, hour, day

2. cow, cat, sheep, mouse, elephant

3. city, country, continent, village, town

4. ocean, river, spring, stream, sea

5. sentence, letter, chapter, word, page

B Try these. Write them in **order**.

1. marched, ran, strolled, walked, jogged

2. giggled, smiled, chuckled, laughed, guffawed

3. roared, whispered, talked, shrieked, shouted

4. hurricane, breeze, wind, draught, gale

5. mountain, slope, hill, molehill, mound

6. warm, hot, cool, boiling, cold

7. terrified, nervous, frightened, alarmed, startled

8. liner, boat, dinghy, tug, ferry

Ordering a story

A Put the sentences in the right **order**.

Ben looked out at the sea of faces as he came out of the door.

Ben was getting very excited as he looked out of the window.

After he had collected his case Ben walked towards the exit.

He was wondering if Aunt Mary would be there to meet him.

They were approaching Manchester airport.

Suddenly he saw the face he was searching for.

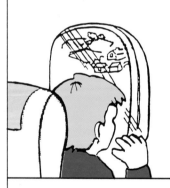

He could see houses and fields as the plane landed.

"Welcome to Manchester," she said.

Aunt Mary was smiling and waving to him.

B Write out the story. Compare your version with a friend's.

Basic Rules of Grammar: Book 4 © Folens

Instructions

A What is wrong with these **instructions**?

1. Take off your clothes and place them in the bath.
2. Put the plug in the plug hole.
3. Turn on the cold water and fill the bath.
4. Make sure the water is not too hot.
5. Hop into the bath.
6. Wash yourself well with toothpaste.
7. Relax and have a sleep.
8. Step out of the bath and let the water out.
9. Wet yourself with a towel until you are dry.
10. Put on a nice set of dirty clothes.

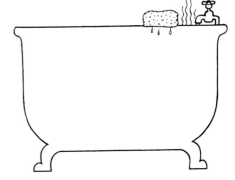

Write a better set of **instructions**.
Remember to punctuate them correctly.

B 1. Write a list of sensible **instructions** for making a sandwich. Number each **instruction**.

2. Re-write the **instructions** so that they are as silly as in **A**.

C 1. Choose something to write **instructions** for. Write silly and sensible **instructions**.

2. Give the silly **instructions** to a partner. Your partner should re-write them to make them sensible.

3. Compare your partner's sensible **instructions** with yours.

Paragraphs

A new **paragraph** is used to show **a change of subject**.

A Here are some sentences about Paul.
Some tell you about his looks, some about his home
and some about his hobbies.

Arrange the sentences in three **paragraphs** starting with:
the way he looks
then where he lives
and lastly his hobbies.

Paul is tall, dark and strong looking.

He has a happy, friendly face and people like him.

Paul lives on a farm near a small town in Scotland.

The farm is big and his father keeps sheep on the hillsides and cows for beef and grows crops.

He has dark hair, dark eyes and sun-tanned skin.

When he cannot go to see his friends he spends his time making wooden models.

His home is near the mountains so he has a long way to go to meet his friends.

Paul likes to listen to pop music and he has a lot of records.

Paul loves the winter and likes to ski down the snowy, mountain slopes.

B Write three **paragraphs** about a famous person.
The **paragraphs** could be about why he or she is famous, his or her looks
and his or her clothes.

Basic Rules of Grammar: Book 4

Making notes

A Read the **information** about hedgehogs.

The hedgehog is a small, prickly animal. It has a coat of sharp pointed prickles called spines on its head and back. These spines protect the hedgehog.

Whenever there is danger the hedgehog just curls up into a ball. Many people are surprised to find out that a hedgehog has a short tail. For such a small creature the hedgehog has strong jaws and sharp teeth. Its favourite foods are insects, worms and snails.

The hedgehog's eyesight is poor. It has a good sense of smell and hearing. The hedgehog is nocturnal. That means it goes out at night to hunt for food. In colder weather it makes a nest in a hollow or hole in the ground and goes to sleep. It sleeps or hibernates throughout the winter.

Copy the chart below to make notes about the important facts:

Appearance	Food	Senses	Other information

B 1. Read **information** from a non-fiction book of your choice.
Decide how you will group the facts. Make notes under headings.

2. Give your notes to a friend.
Ask your friend to use these notes to write a summary of the book.

Test 5

A Re-write these groups of words below in a sensible **order**:

1. October, March, August, December, May

2. talk, mutter, whisper, scream, shout

3. huge, small, big , colossal, tiny

4. seedling, tree, sapling, seed

B 1. Write a set of **instructions** for making a paper aeroplane.
Think carefully. Do not leave anything important out.

2. The sentences in the passage below are in the wrong order.
Re-write the passage in your book correctly.

   He slipped quietly out of bed. Then he opened the front door and made a dash for freedom. It was still quite dark. Sam walked down the stairs, hoping they wouldn't creak. Sam woke early.

C Below are some notes about Mrs Brown.
Use them to help you write a description of her.

Personal appearance	Clothes	Actions
round face	torn dress	carries battered carrier bag
untidy brown hair	red, high-heeled shoes	talks to herself
smiling mouth	wears lots of rings	

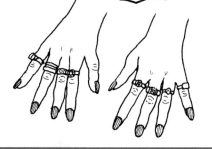

Basic Rules of Grammar: Book 4
© Folens

Homonyms

Homonyms are words that are spelled the same but have different meanings.

Examples:

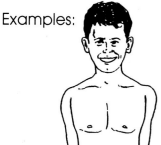
chest

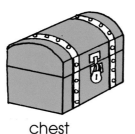
chest

top

top

A Use words from the box to fill the gaps.

| set | ring | hands | box | skip |

1. I cut my [　　　] on a nail.

2. The clock has two [　　　]

3. Here is a [　　　] of golf clubs.

4. The sun will [　　　] at seven o'clock.

5. Two prize fighters will [　　　] tonight.

6. Here is a [　　　] of chocolates.

7. Please [　　　] the bell.

8. She has a [　　　] on each finger.

9. We will [　　　] this page and go on to the next one.

10. I can [　　　] with a rope.

B Which homonyms mean:

1. not heavy and pale?
2. to leave a stationary car and a place to play?
3. a small animal and part of a computer?
4. a plant and to skip on one foot?

C Write sentences that show two meanings of these words:

1. grave   2. spring   3. rest   4. post

Verbs made from nouns

Many **verbs** are made from **nouns**.
Often part of the **noun** is used.
This is called the **root word**.

Examples: solid – **solid**ify
crust – en**crust**.

Sometimes the **noun** is changed and the **root** word is lost.

Example: gold – gild.

A   What **nouns** are these **verbs** made from?

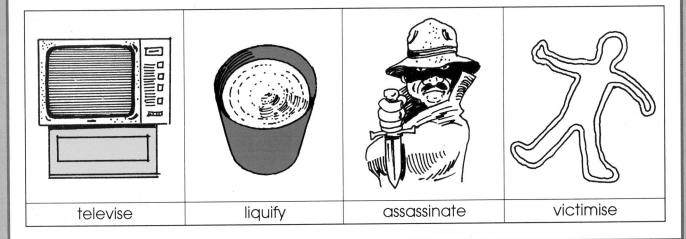

| televise | liquify | assassinate | victimise |

B   Make these **nouns** into **verbs**:

1. peace   2. radius   3. pursuit   4. saliva   5. package

C   What **verbs** are these **nouns** made from?

1. liking, marriage, carriage, carvery

2. repetition, alliance, education, instruction

3. attraction, radiation, cleaner, teacher

4. selection, choice, eraser, election

Prefixes

A **prefix** is added to the **beginning of a word** to **change its meaning**.

Example: **ex** is a **prefix** meaning **out**.

Look at each picture below. Read the word underneath.
Write a sentence to explain what is happening in the picture.

1. **ex**tract	2. **ex**hale	3. **ex**ile
4. **ex**it	5. **ex**haust	6. **ex**port
7. **ex**cavate	8. **ex**hibition	9. **ex**pel

Prefixes

Super is a **prefix** that means **over** or **beyond**.

A Find the ten words in the **super snake**.
Look them up in your dictionary and write their meanings.

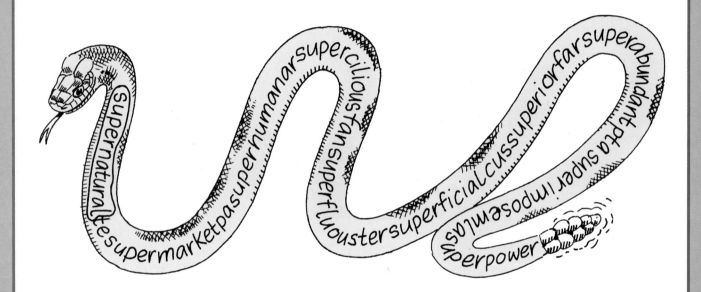

B

admirable	breathtaking	excellent
marvellous	splendid	

You could use one **super** word instead of
any of the above words.

What is it? [＿＿＿＿] b

C What **super** is the manager of other workers in an office?

[＿＿＿＿] sor

D What **super** is the manager of other police officers?

[＿＿＿＿] ant

Suffixes

A **suffix** is added to the **end** of a word.
ish is a **suffix** that can change a **noun** into an **adjective**.

Example: self – self**ish**

A   List all the words in this passage that have the suffix **ish**:

Once there was a selfish giant. He lived in a big castle. He did not like

children playing in his garden. He hated their childish laughter. He was

a very foolish giant because he became very sad and lonely in his

freezing castle without any friends. Then one day he saw a small child

sitting in the branches of a tree. The garden brightened up and

flowers began to grow. The children began to creep back in a sheepish

way into the garden. The giant realised how foolish he had been and

was delighted to hear the childish voices around him. With a tigerish

roar of laughter, he beckoned to them all to come in and play.

B   Find a dictionary definition for each of these words:

1. self**ish**	2. fever**ish**	3. sheep**ish**	4. fiend**ish**
5. child**ish**	6. tiger**ish**	7. elf**ish**	8. churl**ish**
9. Finn**ish**	10. baby**ish**	11. wasp**ish**	12. girl**ish**
13. fool**ish**	14. boy**ish**	15. Turk**ish**	16. imp**ish**

Suffixes

Suffixes can make **roots** of **verbs** or **nouns** into **occupations**.
er, **or**, **ist** and **ian** are all suffixes.

Example: doct**or**.

A Finish the occupations below:

1. teach [ ]

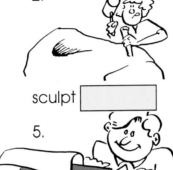

2. sculpt [ ]

3. pian [ ]

4. sail [ ]

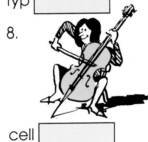

5. typ [ ]

driv [ ]

7. politic [ ]

8. cell [ ]

9. conduct [ ]

B **er**, **ian** and **ist** can be added to place names to make **nouns** for people.

1. A person from London. London [ ] 2. A person from Venice. Venet [ ]

3. A person from Darwin. Darwin [ ] 4. A person from Boston. Boston [ ]

C Write a sentence that describes what these do:

1. a flautist
2. an escapologist
3. a humanist
4. a Buddhist
5. an archaeologist
6. a philatelist
7. a Mancunian
8. an Evertonian
9. an Austrian
10. an Italian
11. a Liverpudlian
12. a physician
13. an undertaker
14. an adviser
15. a producer
16. a publisher
17. a lecturer
18. an editor

Basic Rules of Grammar: Book 4

Syllabication

Words can be split into separate **syllables** to make them **easier to read**.

These words have **one syllable**: cat, rot, pan, stand.

Words with **one syllable** are called **monosyllabic** words.

These words have **two syllables**: cat/tle, man/sion, pa/per.

Words with **two or more syllables** are called **polysyllabic** words.

A   List the **polysyllabic** words in this box:

rattle	out	unicorn	snap
unhappy	somebody	bad	care
happy	nevertheless	invisible	personality
hover	position	rap	responsibility
general	rain	sing	unbelievable
publishing	exercise	illustration	computer

B   Sort these words.
Copy and complete the chart.

bank	dream	pastrami	hexagon
flower	please	petrify	triangular
dozen	plantation	politician	hexagonal
eliminate	extra	bonus	square
construction	peaceful	band	oblong
elevation	underestimate	adjacent	diagonally
radius	overjoyed	triangle	vertically
potato	blameless	quadrilateral	horizontal

One syllable	Two syllables	Three syllables	Four syllables	Five syllables

C   Find a paragraph in a book that is about ten lines long.
Make lists of all the words in it with **one syllable**, **two syllables**, **three syllables**, **four syllables**, **five syllables** and more.

Test 6

A What are these **homonyms**?

1. Matched and healthy.
2. Pull and use a pencil to make a picture.
3. A hill and a direction for descending.
4. An animal and to follow.
5. A curved shape and a weapon with arrows.

dog
bow
down
draw
fit

B Make these **nouns** into **verbs**:

1. case   2. compass   3. liquid   4. beauty

C What **verbs** are these **nouns** made from?

1. realisation   2. mower   3. cultivation   4. entry

D Write five words that begin with these **prefixes**:

1. in   2. ex   3. un

E Write five words that end with these **suffixes**:

1. ish   2. ful   3. or

F Copy and complete the chart with your own examples:

Words with:				
One syllable	Two syllables	Three syllables	Four syllables	Five syllables